Chip had a box.

"This is my robot," he said.

"Can you see it?"

"This is a leg," said Chip.

"Can you see the robot?"

"This is an arm," said Chip.

"Can you see my robot?"

"Can you see it, yet?" said Chip.

"No," said Biff.

"This is the head," said Chip.

"Now can you see my robot?"

"We can see it now!" said Biff.